Gabrielle
Buttiho

Mackenzie
Duval

Katiner

Thomsen

J. Caso

C.

BreahWong

Meaghan
Forget

Emanuella. G

Kaitlyn
seames

Christine
Sprow

Bmy

Kim M.

Lily C.-H.

Kaitlyn
Seames

Emanuella.a

Meaghan
Hogent

Shyann
Lebeau

Kim M.

Benny

E:J C.-w

WHEN I THINK OF THE ALPHABET...

Illustrations by Kelly Daly

A COLLECTION BY YOUNG AUTHORS

When I Think of the Alphabet
Copyright © Domnizelles Publications Inc. All Rights Reserved.
First edition.

ISBN: 978-0-9878554-9-7
ISBN (E-PUBLISHING): 978-1-927815-01-4

Library and Archives Canada Cataloguing in Publication information is
available upon request.

Published by Domnizelles Publications Inc.,
845 Cure-Labelle, Suite 300
Laval, Quebec,
H7V 2V2
Canada
www.domnizelles.com

Illustrations by Kelly Daly
Cover and book design by Ranilo Cabo
Edited by Vicki Fraser and Diana Antonacci

Printed and bound in Canada.

When I Think of the Alphabet, I Think of…

When I think of the alphabet, I think of **A**mazing **B**abysitters, **C**razy **D**ogs, **E**xpressive

Flamingos, **G**orgeous **H**ats, **I**mportant **J**anitors, **K**ind **L**eopards, **M**assive **N**injas, **O**riginal

Packages, **Q**uick **R**ats, **S**arcastic **T**igers, **U**gly **V**eins, **W**hite **X**-rays, and **Y**ellow **Z**ippers.

When I think of the alphabet, I think of twenty-six letters mixed in a song.

You can make a lot of words with the letters of the alphabet. Letters build words. Words produce

sentences. Sentences construct paragraphs and paragraphs create stories.

Now read this book from A to Z…

Megan Baker

3

Aa

When I think of the letter A, I think of amazing, ambitious, aspiring artists.

I think of awful, angry, awkward aliens.

I think of addition, Africa, airplanes, androids, animals, Antarctica, ants, apartments, apples,

aquariums, astronauts, and Australia.

Alexandra Asprakis

Bb

When I think of the letter B, I think of big, buzzing bumble bees, breezing by briskly.

I think of big, beautiful, bouncing belugas.

I think of barbecues, baseballs, basketballs, bears, Belgium, bikes, birds, boats, books,

blackberries, Brazil, and buttons.

Victor Berry

Cc

When I think of the letter C, I think of cautious, colour-changing, camouflaged chameleons.

I think of cute, cuddly, caramel and cream-coloured cats.

I think of camels, cameras, Canada, carrots, cars, children, Chile, China, clocks, computers, crabs, and crayons.

Kaitlyn Seames

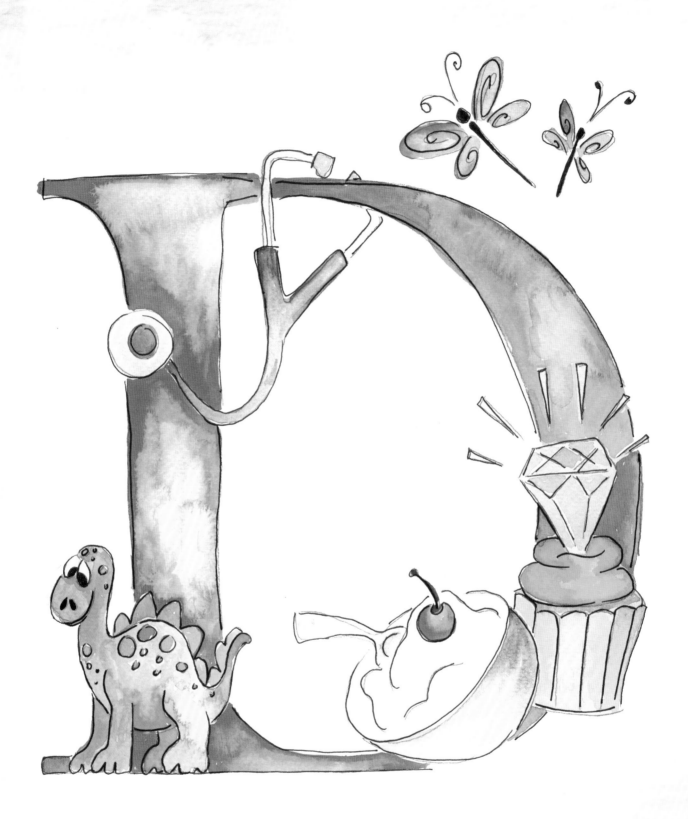

Dd

When I think of the letter D, I think of divine, delightful and delicious desserts.

I think of dazzling, delicate, desirable diamonds.

I think of danger, deer, Denmark, desks, dinosaurs, doctors, dogs, dolphins, dragonflies, dragons, drawings, and drums.

Evangelos Vavinis

Ee

When I think of the letter E, I think of enchanting, exquisite, extremely expensive, emerald

earrings.

I think of excited, enthusiastic, energetic, entertaining elves.

I think of eagles, ears, eggplants, eggs, elbows, electric eels, elephants, elevators, England,

Europe, Everest, and exams.

Moesha Louis-Bastien

Ff

When I think of the letter F, I think of fast, fascinating, flying, flashing fireflies.

I think of fabulous, flavourful French fries.

I think of family, fashion, feet, Finland, fire, fish, flashlights, fog, football, France, Fridays, and the future.

Antoine Lambert

Gg

When I think of the letter G, I think of gross, gooey, gummy gum.

I think of gorgeous, giggling, gifted girls.

I think of games, gardens, ghosts, giraffes, glaciers, glasses, gloves, goldfish, gorillas,

grandparents, Guatemala, and guitars.

Gabrielle Buttino

Hh

When I think of the letter H, I think of happy, heartfelt, helpful hellos.

I think of hilarious, hefty, humongous hippos.

I think of Haiti, hamsters, hats, hearts, holidays, Holland, honey, hopscotch, horses, houses,

hula hoops, and huskies.

Karina Pinelli

Ii

When I think of the letter I, I think of immense, interesting, inspiring inventions.

I think of incredible, impressive, intriguing iguanas.

I think of icicles, icing, igloos, images, inchworms, India, initials, ink, insects, instruments,

Israel, and Italy.

Mackenzie Duval

Jj

When I think of the letter J, I think of juggling, joking, jumpy jesters.

I think of jamming, jazzy, jumbo jukeboxes.

I think of jaguars, jail, jam, Jamaica, Japan, jeans, jellyfish, jets, jewels, journeys, juice, and

jungles.

Justin Caso

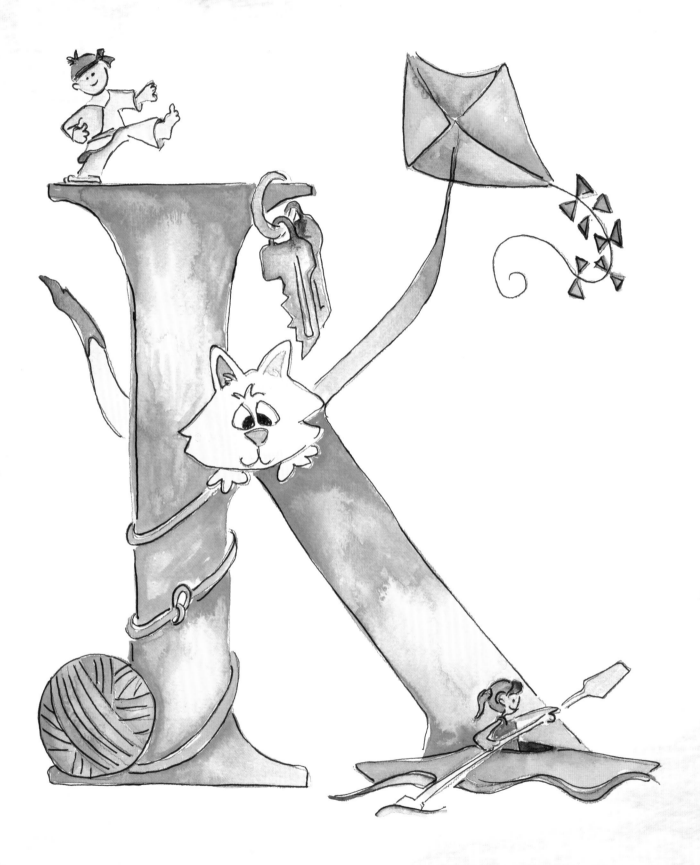

Kk

When I think of the letter K, I think of kind, kissable, keen kittens.

I think of knowledgeable, klutzy, kind-hearted, kindergarten kids.

I think of kangaroos, karate, kayaks, kazoos, Kenya, keys, kings, kites, kiwis, knights, koalas,

and knots.

Christina Lepore

Ll

When I think of the letter L, I think of legendary, loving, loyal, licking lions.

I think of lovely, long, lavender lilies.

I think of ladders, ladybugs, lakes, leaves, letters, lettuce, libraries, lightning, lizards, lobsters,

lollipops, and Luxembourg.

Lily Cartman

Mm

When I think of the letter M, I think of marvelous, magnificent, melodious music.

I think of messy, mouth-watering, melted, marshmallows.

I think of machines, magicians, maps, marbles, mermaids, meteors, microscopes, monkeys,

monsters, moose, Morocco, and muscles.

Vincent Morency

Nn

When I think of the letter N, I think of numerous, narrow, nibbled, "nummy" noodles.

I think of nice, necessary, nurturing nannies.

I think of nails, names, naps, nature, Nepal, nests, nets, nights, ninjas, Norway, noses, and

numbers.

Émilie Dagenais-Roberge

Oo

When I think of the letter O, I think of outrageous, overpowering, oversized oceans.

I think of organized, overwhelming, outstanding orchestras.

I think of Oceania, October, octopuses, olives, operas, oranges, organs, ostriches, ovals, owls,

oxygen and oysters.

Thamsen Commier

Pp

When I think of the letter P, I think of pouting, playful, pleasant, protective puppies.

I think of prissy, perfect, popular, pink and purple princesses.

I think of Pakistan, Panama, pandas, papayas, pearls, peppermint, pickles, pictures, pirates,

playgrounds, pools, and puzzles.

Emanuella Gumelli

Qq

When I think of the letter Q, I think of quiet, qualified, quick-witted, quaint queens.

I think of quick, querying, questioning quizzes.

I think of Qatar, quacks, quadruplets, quails, quakes, quarrels, quarries, quarters, questions, quests, quicksand, and quilts.

Pietro Rainone

Rr

When I think of the letter R, I think of rushing, rambunctious, road-running rhinoceroses.

I think of rising, racket-making, rusty-red roosters.

I think of rabbits, rain, rainbows, ramps, rats, riddles, rings, Romania, ropes, roses, rugs, and

rulers.

Jordan Goyer

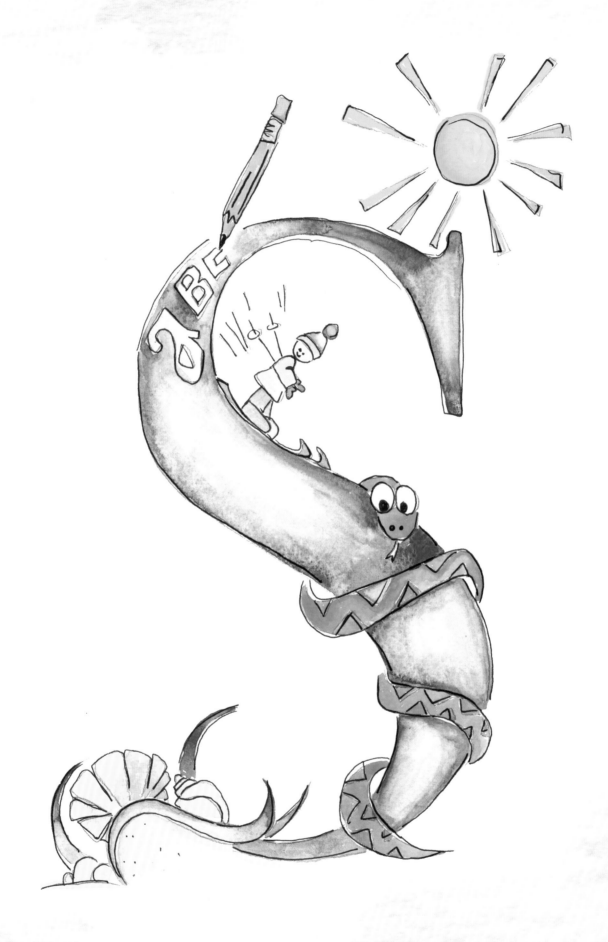

Ss

When I think of the letter S, I think of six, silly, slushy snowmen.

I think of smooth, sleek, slithering, sneaky snakes.

I think of sand, seas, secrets, September, school, skeletons, skis, soccer, Spain, stop signs,

sunshine and Sweden.

Kimberly Morin

Tt

When I think of the letter T, I think of tiny, talkative, tattling toddlers.

I think of tremendously terrifying, thrilling, toothy tigers.

I think of tangerines, tiaras, toucans, toys, trains, trees, trucks, trumpets, tulips, Tunisia, tunnels,

and turtles.

Breah Wong

Uu

When I think of the letter U, I think of underestimated, unbelievably unique, uplifting unicorns.

I think of unsteady, unstable, unusual unicycles.

I think of Ukraine, ukuleles, umbrellas, umpires, uncles, underarms, underpants, uniforms,

unions, the United States of America, the Universe, and universities.

Meaghan Forget

Vv

When I think of the letter V, I think of valiant, vowing, valued veterans.

I think of violent, vivid, virtual video games.

I think of valleys, vaults, vehicles, Venezuela, venom, Venus, Vietnam, violets, violins,

vocabulary, vocalists, and voyages.

Shayan Khodadadi

Ww

When I think of the letter W, I think of wild, wondrous, wandering, wet wolves.

I think of wrinkled, wrestling, wiggly worms.

I think of wagons, walls, waterfalls, watermelons, webs, whales, wheels, wigs, windows, winter,

wishes, and the world.

Elliot Desrosiers

Xx, Yy and Zz

When I think of the letter X, I think of e**X**cellent, e**X**travagent, e**X**quisite xylophones.

When I think of the letter Y, I think of yappy, youthful Yorkshire terriers.

When I think of the letter Z, I think of zany, zesty, zigzagging zebras.

I think of the end of the alphabet!

Maya Ben Ayed